play BASS with...
BON JOVI

Exclusive Distributors:
Music Sales Limited, 8/9 Frith Street, London W1D 3JB, England.
Music Sales Pty Limited, 120 Rothschild Avenue, Rosebery, NSW 2018, Australia.

Order No. AM976272
ISBN 0-7119-9796-9
This book © Copyright 2002 by Wise Publications.

Compiled by Nick Crispin.
Music arranged by Paul Townsend.
Music processed by Paul Ewers Music Design.
Cover photograph courtesy of WireImage.
Printed in the United Kingdom by Caligraving Limited, Thetford, Norfolk.
CD recorded, mixed and mastered by Jonas Persson.
Guitars by Arthur Dick.
Bass Guitar by Paul Townsend.
Drums by Brett Morgan.

www.musicsales.com

Wise Publications *London / New York / Paris / Sydney / Copenhagen / Berlin / Madrid / Tokyo*

BASS GUITAR TABLATURE EXPLAINED

Bass Tablature *is a four-line staff that graphically represents the bass fingerboard. By placing a number on the appropriate line, the string and fret of any note can be indicated. The number 0 represents an open string. For example:*

3rd string, 3rd fret   4th string, open

SLIDE (not restruck): *Strike the first note and then slide the same fret-hand finger up or down to the second note.*

SLIDE (with restrike): *Same as previous slide, except the second note is struck.*

SLIDE: *Slide up to the note indicated from a few notes below.*

SLIDE: *Strike the note indicated and slide up an indefinite number of frets.*

HAMMER-ON: *Strike the first (lower) note with one finger, then sound the higher note (on the same string) with another finger by fretting it without picking.*

PULL-OFF: *Place both fingers on the notes to be sounded. Strike the first note and without picking, pull the finger off to sound the second lower note.*

PALM-MUTE: *The note is partially muted by the pick hand lightly touching the string(s) just before the bridge.*

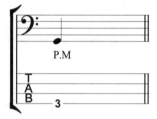

MUFFLED-STRINGS: *A percussive sound is produced by laying the left hand across the string(s) without depressing it to the fretboard.*

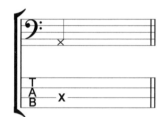

BEND (half step): *Strike the note and bend up a semi-tone (half step).*

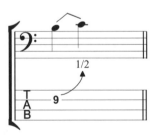

BEND & RELEASE: *Strike the note and bend up as indicated, then release back to the original note.*

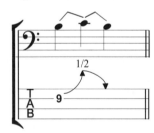

PRE-BEND: *Bend the note as indicated then strike it.*

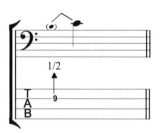

PRE-BEND & RELEASE: *Bend the note as indicated. Strike it and release the note back to the original pitch.*

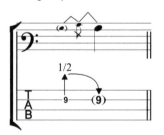

TRILLS: *Very rapidly alternate between the notes indicated by continuously hammering on and pulling off.*

VIBRATO: *The string is vibrated by rapidly bending and releasing the note with the fretting hand.*

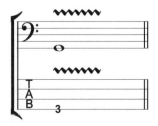

NATURAL HARMONIC: *Strike the note while the fret-hand lightly touches the string directly over the fret indicated.*

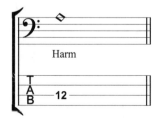

TREMOLO PICKING: *The note is picked as rapidly and continuously as possible.*

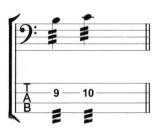

NOTE: *The speed of any bend is indicated by the music notation and tempo.*

EVERYDAY

Words & Music by Jon Bon Jovi, Richie Sambora & Andreas Carlsson

4 or 5 string bass

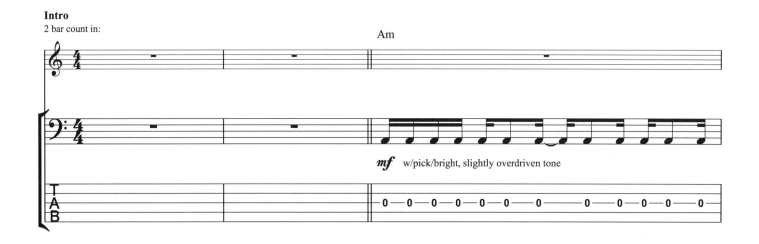

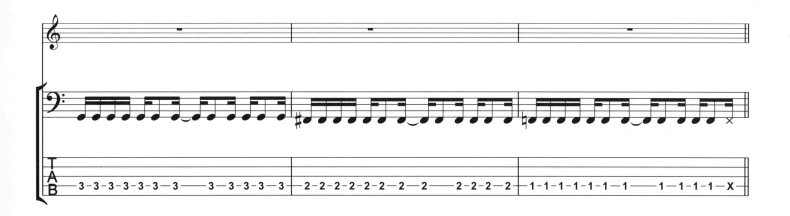

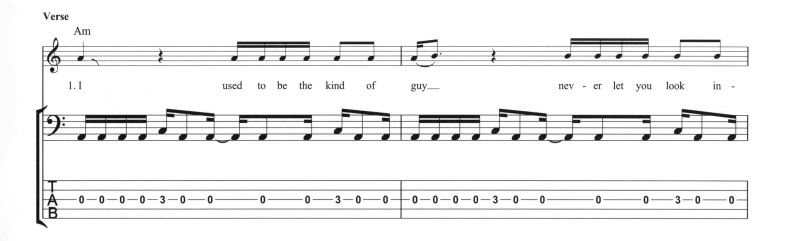

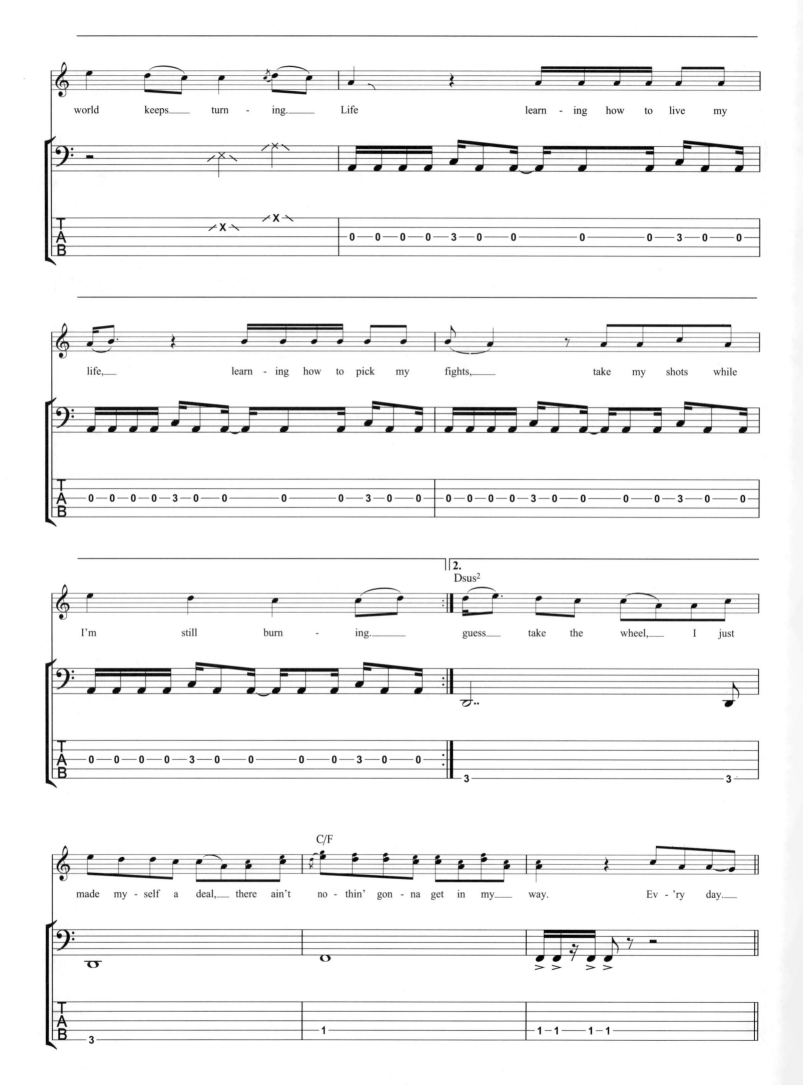

Gtr. solo

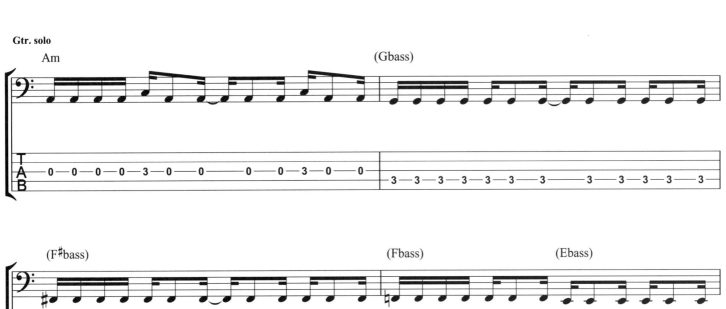

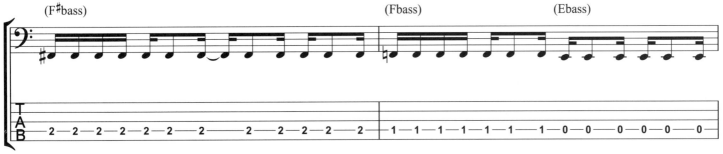

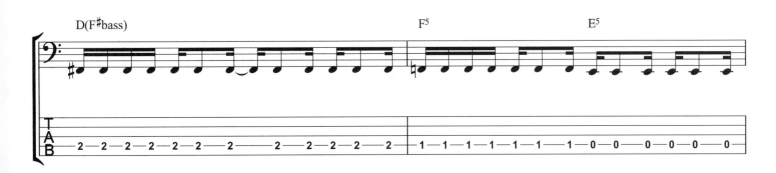

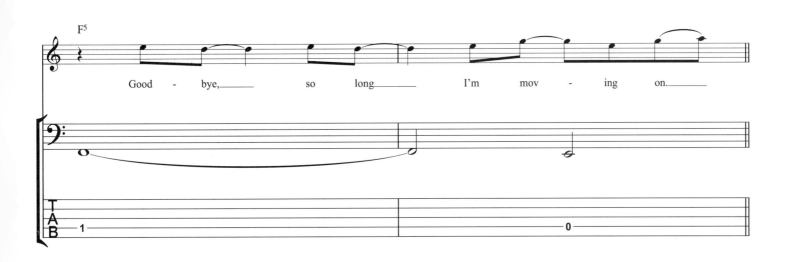

Good - bye,_____ so long_____ I'm mov - ing on._____

HEY GOD

Words & Music by Jon Bon Jovi & Richie Sambora

4 or 5 string bass

Intro
2 bar count in:

1. Hey   God, I'm

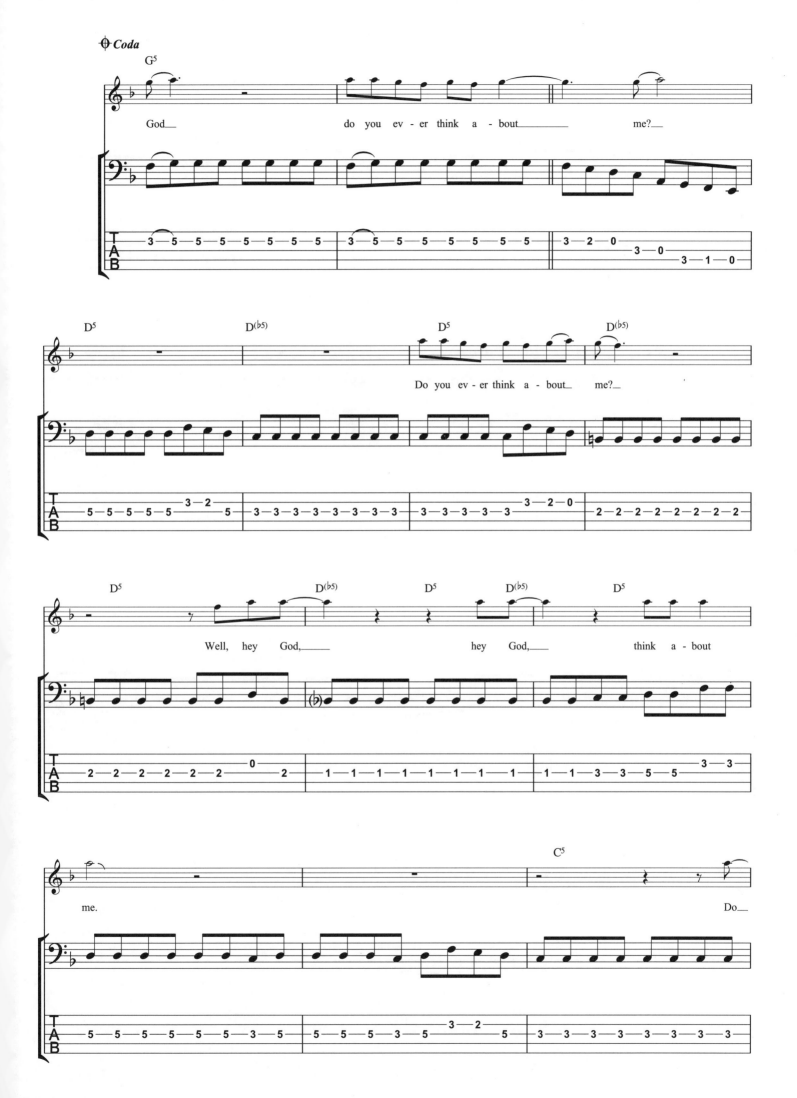

IT'S MY LIFE

Words & Music by Jon Bon Jovi, Richie Sambora & Max Martin

4 or 5 string bass

Intro
2 bar count in:

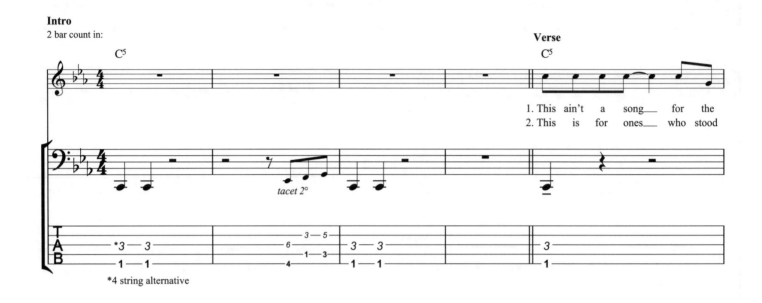

*4 string alternative

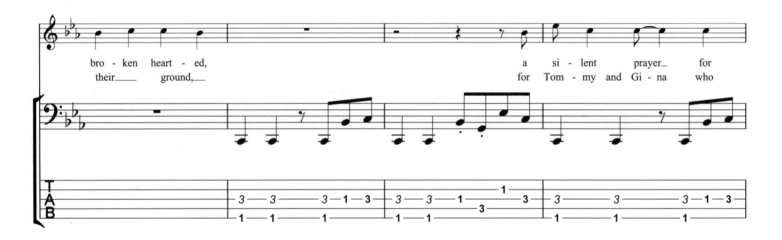

ONE WILD NIGHT

Words & Music by Jon Bon Jovi, Richie Sambora & Desmond Child

4 or 5 string bass

Intro
2 bar count in:

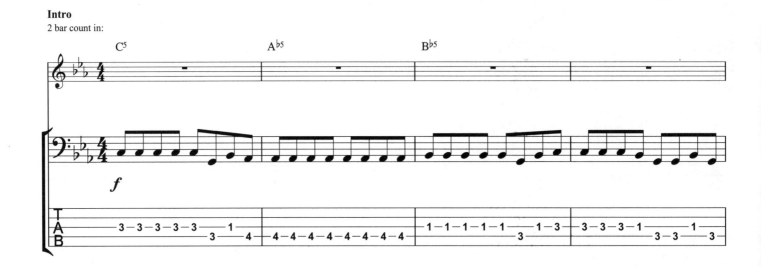

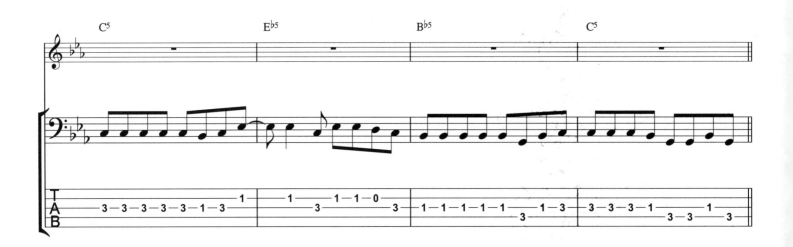

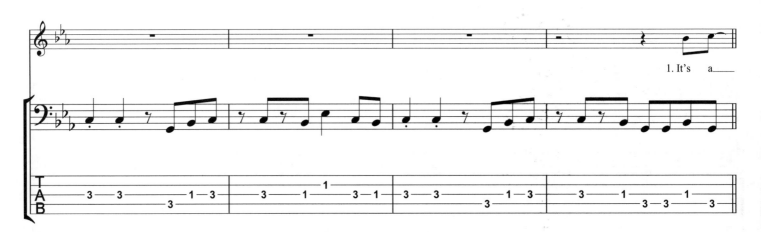

*4 string alternative

SOMETHING FOR THE PAIN

Words & Music by Jon Bon Jovi, Richie Sambora & Desmond Child

4 or 5 string bass

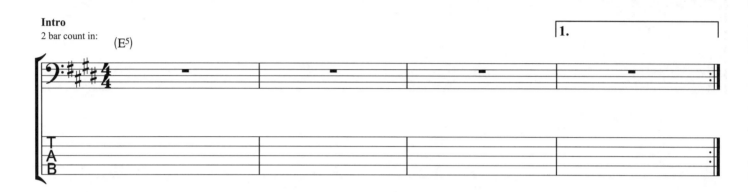

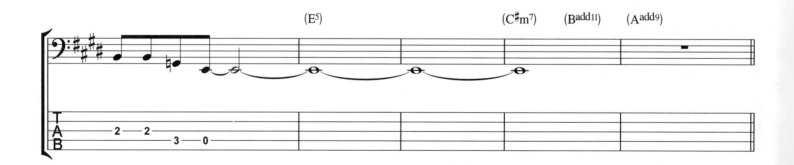

through the night,__ make me feel al - right,__ some - thing like__ you._____

1. Come on, come on, cme on.__

2. Come on, on, come on, come on.

Gtr. solo

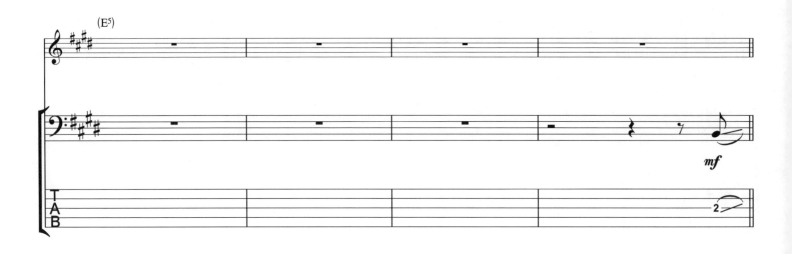

Verse

3. Pull me un - der through my veins____ to a place where I feel no pain. Be the pil - low un - der my head,

(Help____ I'm fall - ing. Night____ is

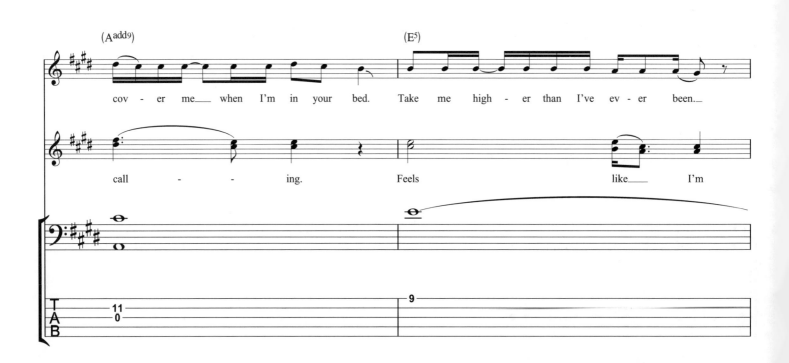

cov - er me____ when I'm in your bed. Take me high - er than I've ev - er been.____

call - - ing. Feels like____ I'm

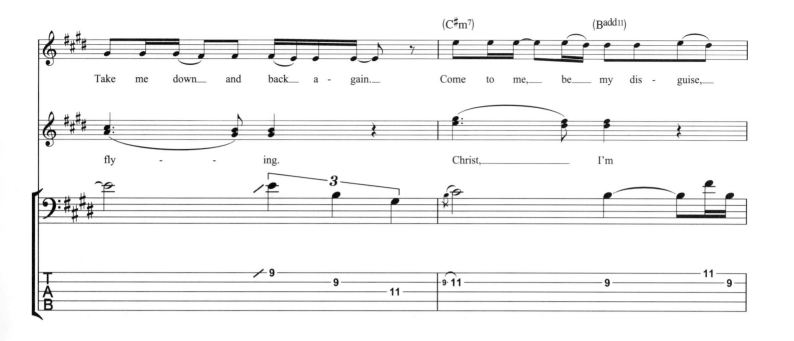

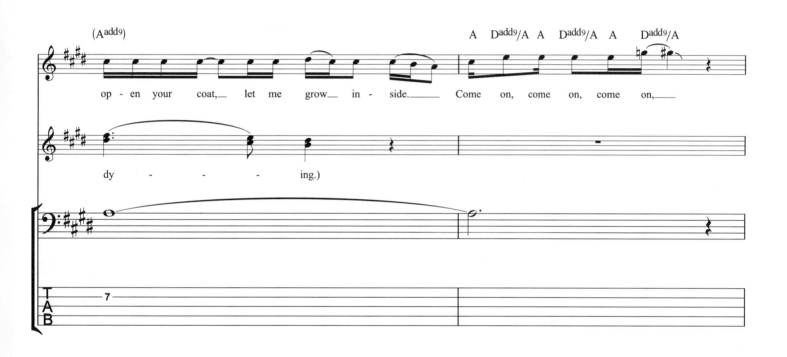

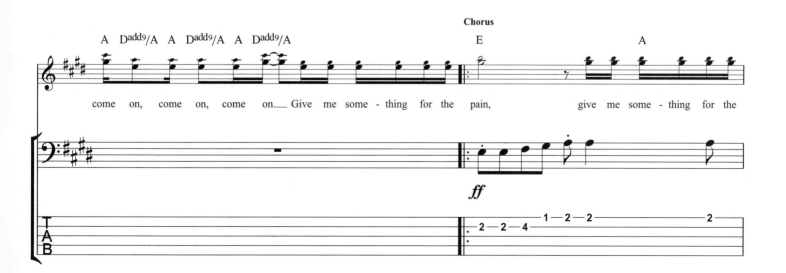

THIS AIN'T A LOVE SONG

Words & Music by Jon Bon Jovi, Richie Sambora & Desmond Child

4 or 5 string bass

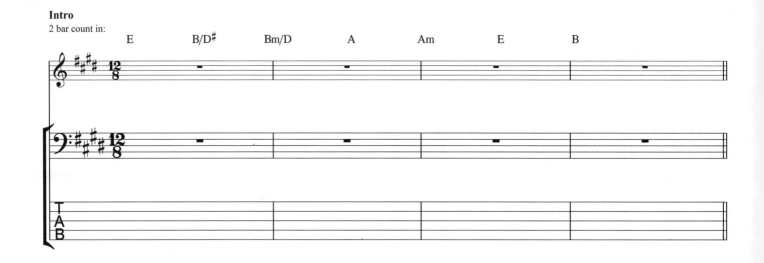

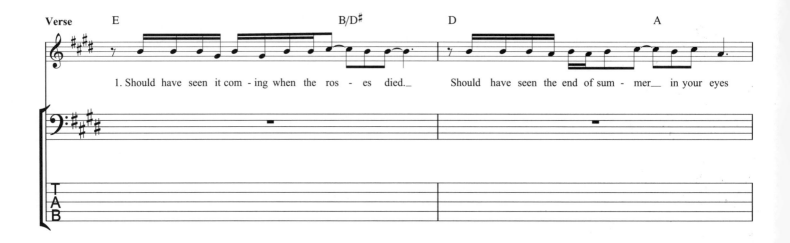

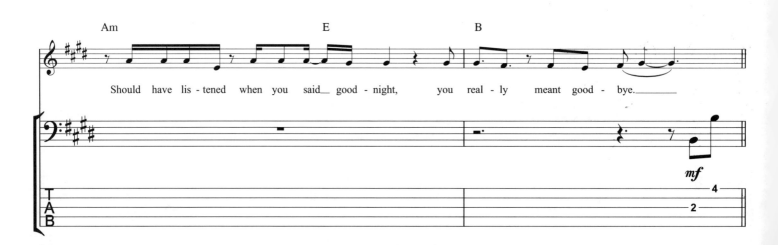